MIGHTY
MACHINES

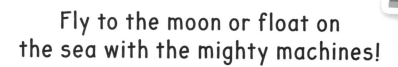

Fly to the moon or float on
the sea with the mighty machines!

•

Use pens, pencils and stickers to complete
the fun activities on each page.

•

Where there is a missing sticker, you will see
an empty shape. Search your sticker pages
to find the missing sticker.

Don't forget to press out some cool stencils
and a fun puzzle to complete from the
card pages at the back of the book!

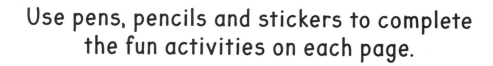

make
believe
ideas

Big digger

Join the dots to finish the digger. Then, count to five!

Sticker a yellow hard hat to finish the pattern.

High in the sky

Search the skies for the things below.

1 helicopter 2 aeroplanes 3 hot-air balloons

Machine maths

Count the vehicles to finish the sums.

1 + 1 = ...

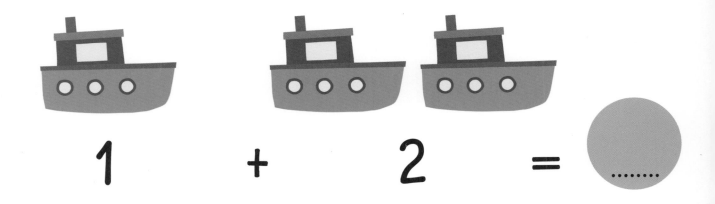

1 + 2 = ...

1 + 3 = ...

Train track

Use a pencil to trace the path to the train station.

Start here!

How many birds can you count? Write the answer. ....

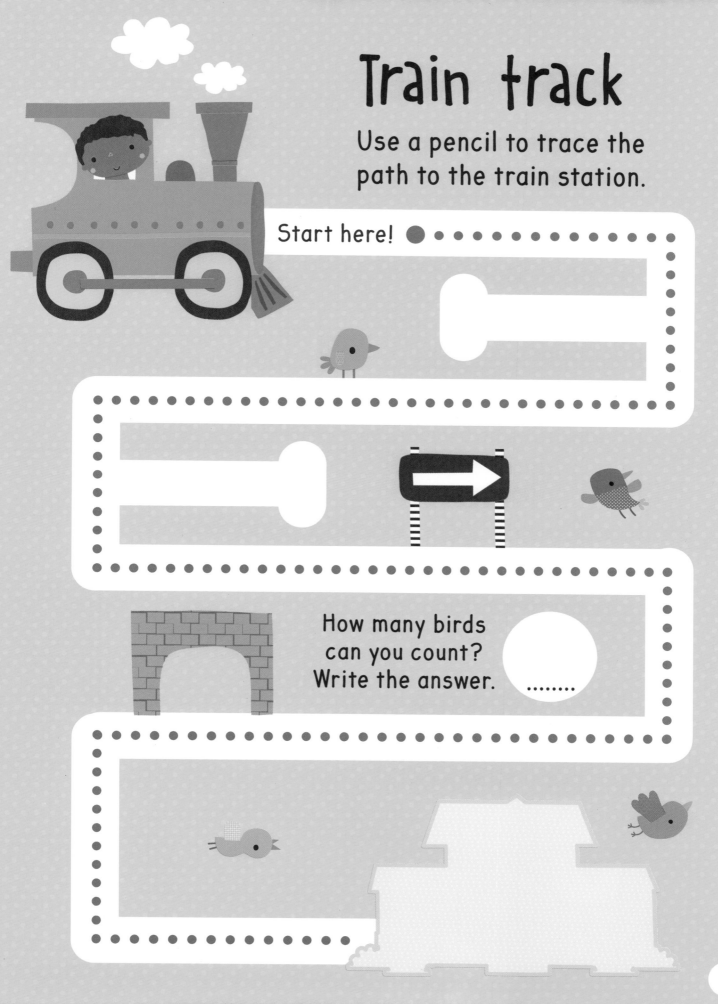

Fire engine fun

Colour the fire engine. Use the coloured dots as a guide.

FIRE

Perfect pairs

Draw lines to match the drivers to their vehicles.

Trophy tangle

Follow the lines to see
who won the race!

Odd One Out

Circle the one that doesn't belong in each row.

Rush hour

Sticker more vehicles on the busy road.

Beep!

Bobbing boat

Use colour to finish the scene.

Spot the difference

Find three differences between the scenes.

Sticker the star when you have finished and say, "I did it!"

Colour and go!

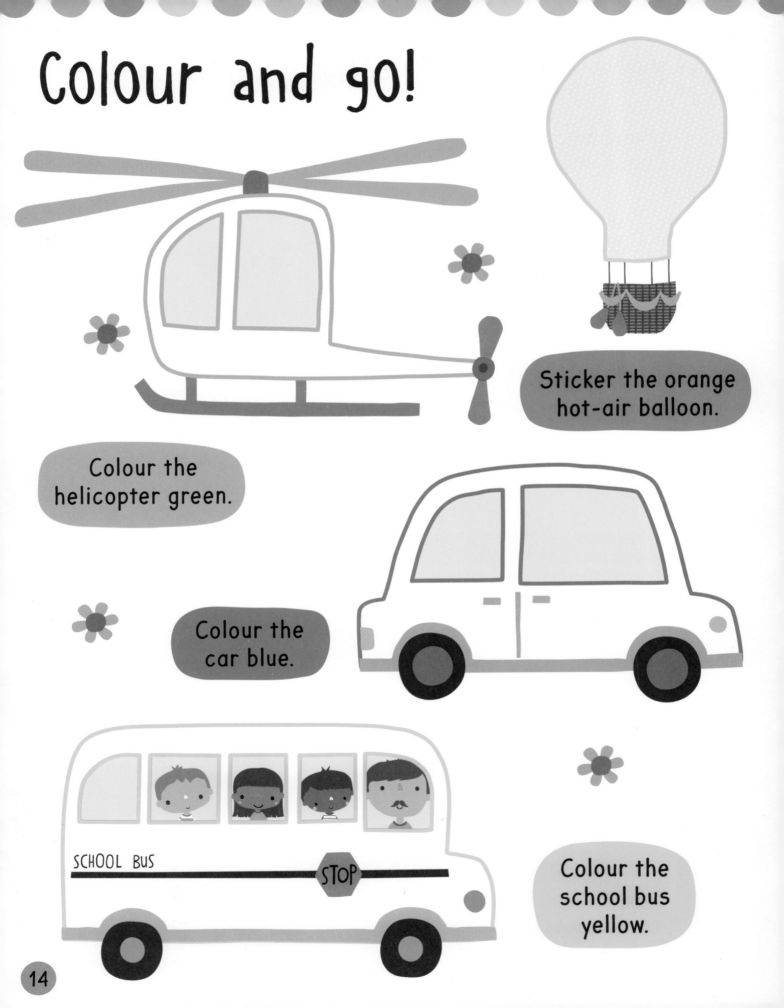

Sticker the orange hot-air balloon.

Colour the helicopter green.

Colour the car blue.

SCHOOL BUS

STOP

Colour the school bus yellow.

Happy halves

Find the stickers to finish the vehicles.

BIG TRUCK

Rocket race

Trace the lines to finish the rocket.
Then, colour it in.

Whirring wheels

Press out the stencils. Use them to draw your own vehicles in the book or wherever you like!

Up in the air

Press out the puzzle pieces and mix them up. Now, put the pieces back together to make this picture.